1.00

RAVETTE PUBLISHING

First published in the UK by Ravette Publishing Ltd 1999

Printed and bound for Ravette Publishing Ltd
Unit 3, Tristar Centre,
Star Road, Partridge Green,
West Sussex RH13 8RA

by Casterman, Belgium

ISBN: 1 85304 989 1

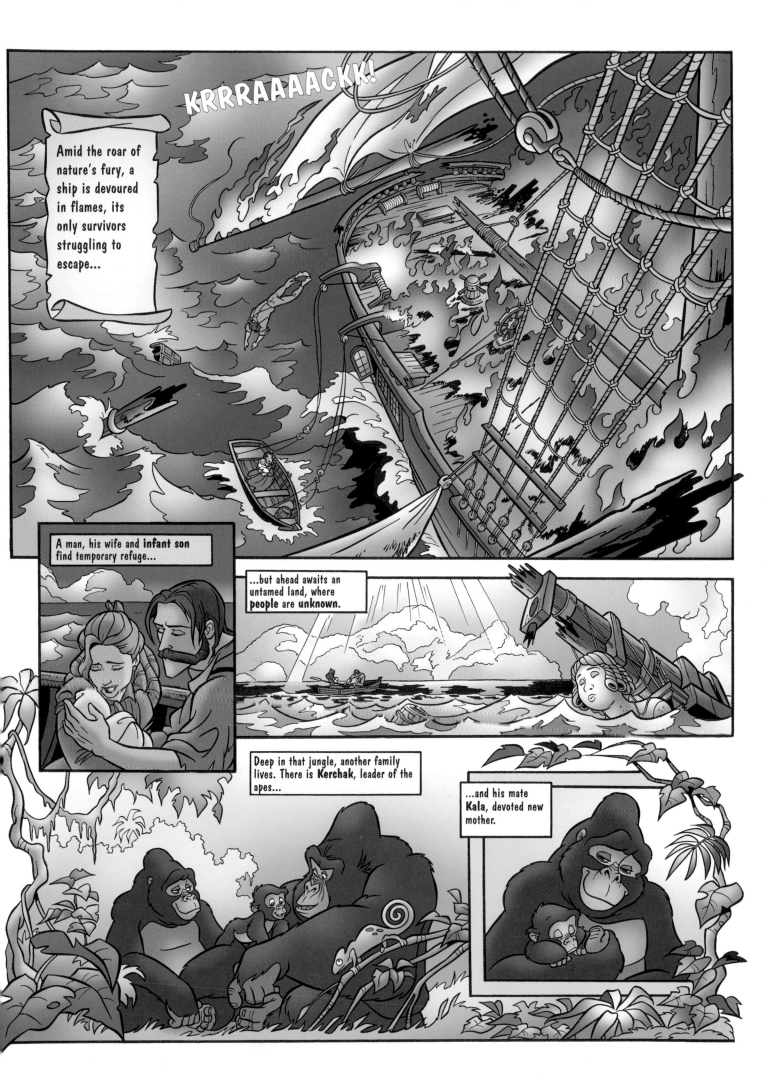

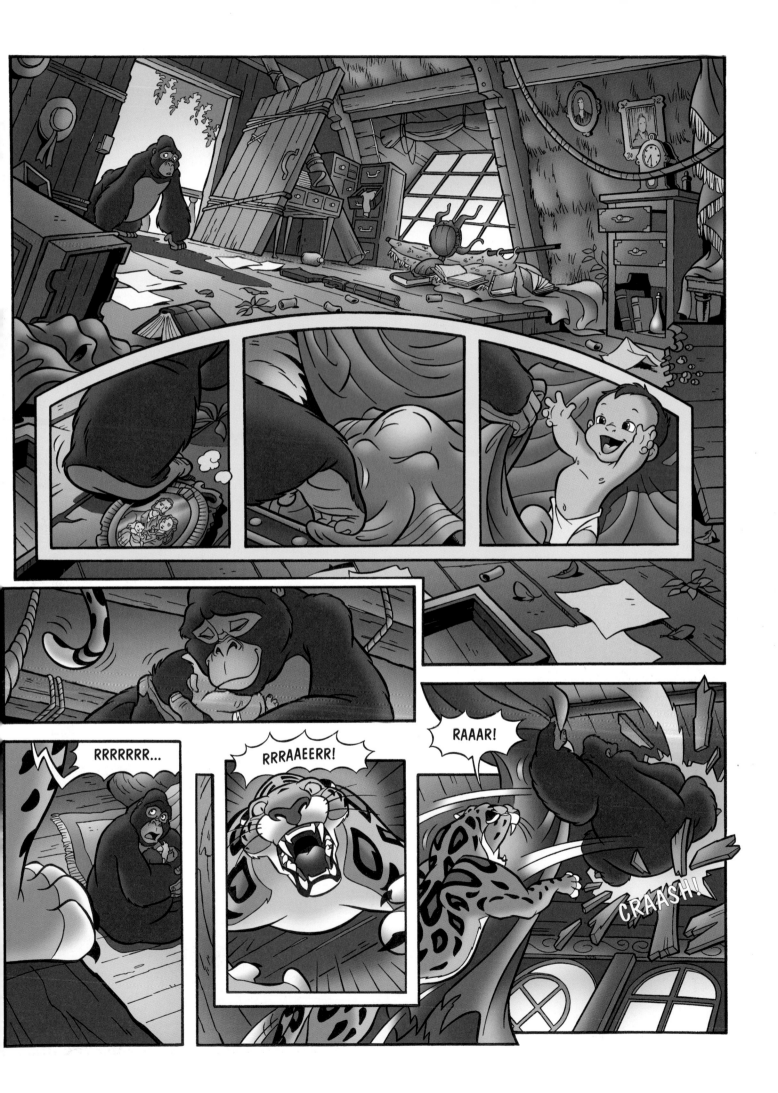

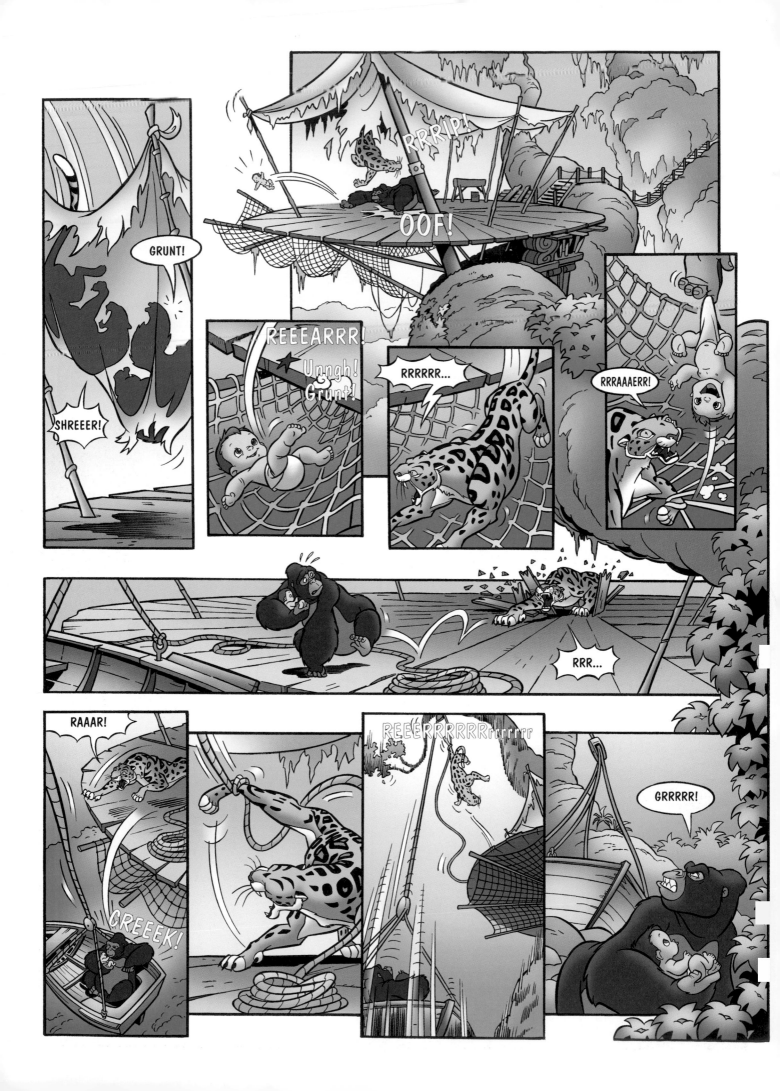

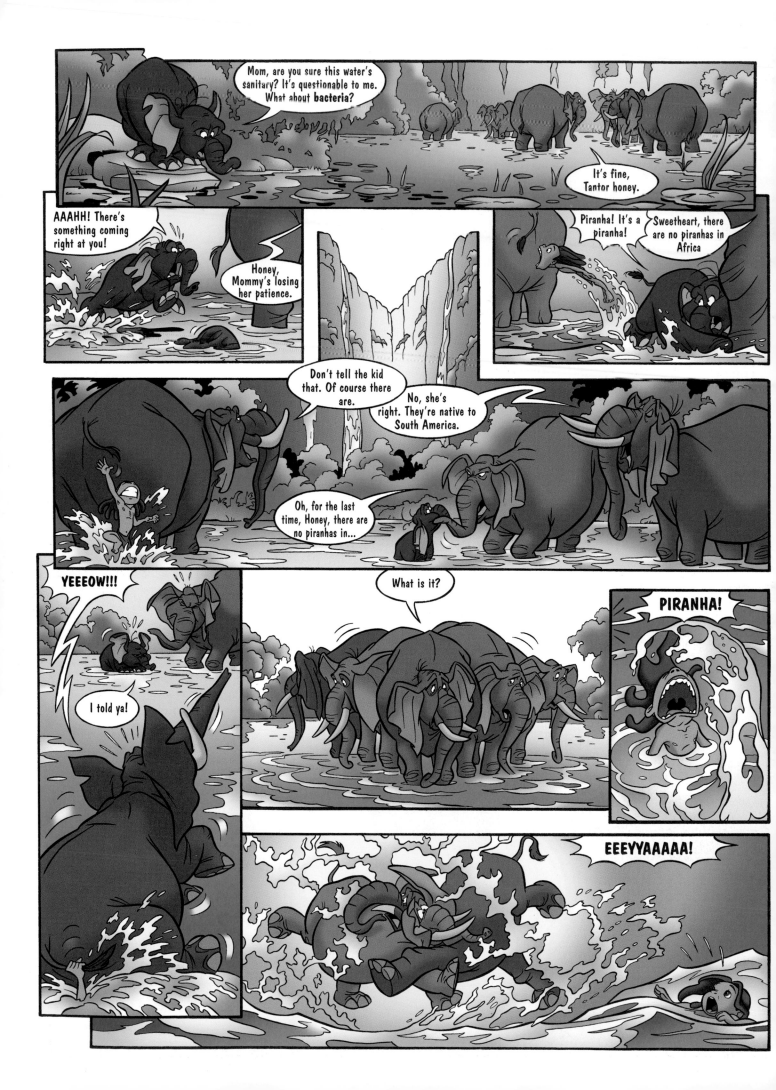

Tarzan!

We were playing, and well-- I'm sorry, Kerchak. It was an accident.

You almost **killed** someone!

He's only a child. He'll learn.

You can't **learn** to be one of us! He will **never** fit in this **family**.

Tarzan!

Tarzan. What are you doing?

Why am I so **different**? Kerchak said I don't belong in the family!

Never mind what Kerchak said.

But **look** at me!

I am, Tarzan. I see two eyes, like mine... And a **nose**... somewhere...

Ah! Here it is!

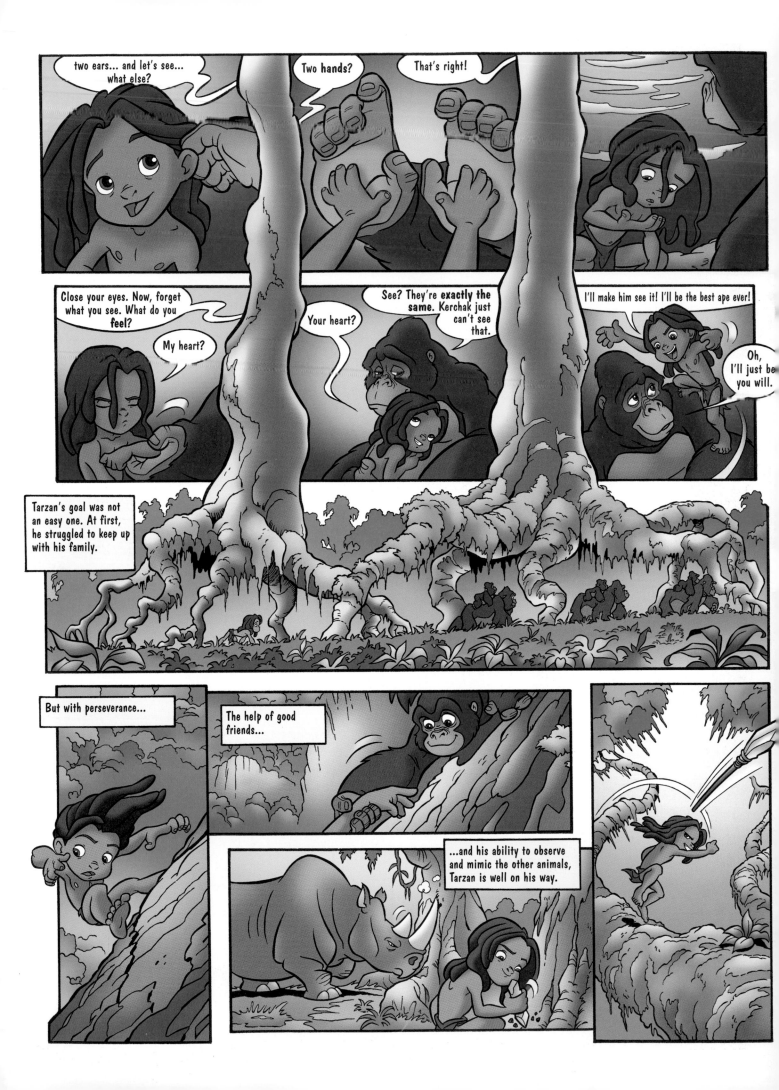

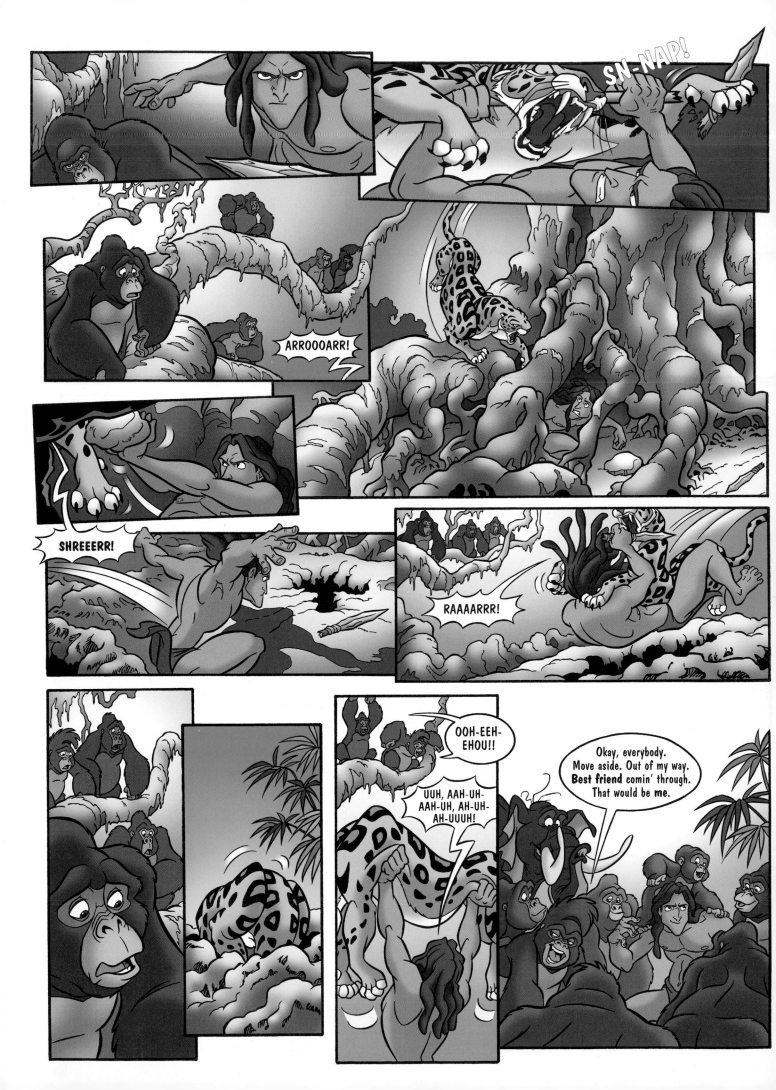

You may be willing to risk our safety, but **I'm** not. Protect your family and stay away from them.

But Kerchak, you're not giving them a chance.

Why didn't you tell me there were creatures that look like me? How can I be your son when I look like them?

It doesn't matter. You are one of us! You are my son.

Kala, you have to tell him.

But Kala can't bring herself to tell Tarzan the truth.

He was this close, Daddy, staring at me, as if he'd never seen another human before. And **his** eyes were intense and focused and... I've never seen such eyes...

Of all the ridiculous--! Professor, you are here to find gorillas! Not indulge some **girlish fantasy**--

What fantasy? I **didn't** imagine him! Tarzan is--

...real.

It's h-- It's him-- It's --Tarzan!

Professor! Jane! Stand back!

No!

Clay-ton.

KA-BANG!

Have we... met? How does he know my name?

He doesn't. He thinks it means the sound of a **gunshot**.

Absolutely fascinating! Moves like an ape, but looks like a man. He could be the **missing link**!

Or our **link** to the gorillas! WHERE ARE THE GORILLAS?